Place Personalized
"Dedication" Sticker
Here

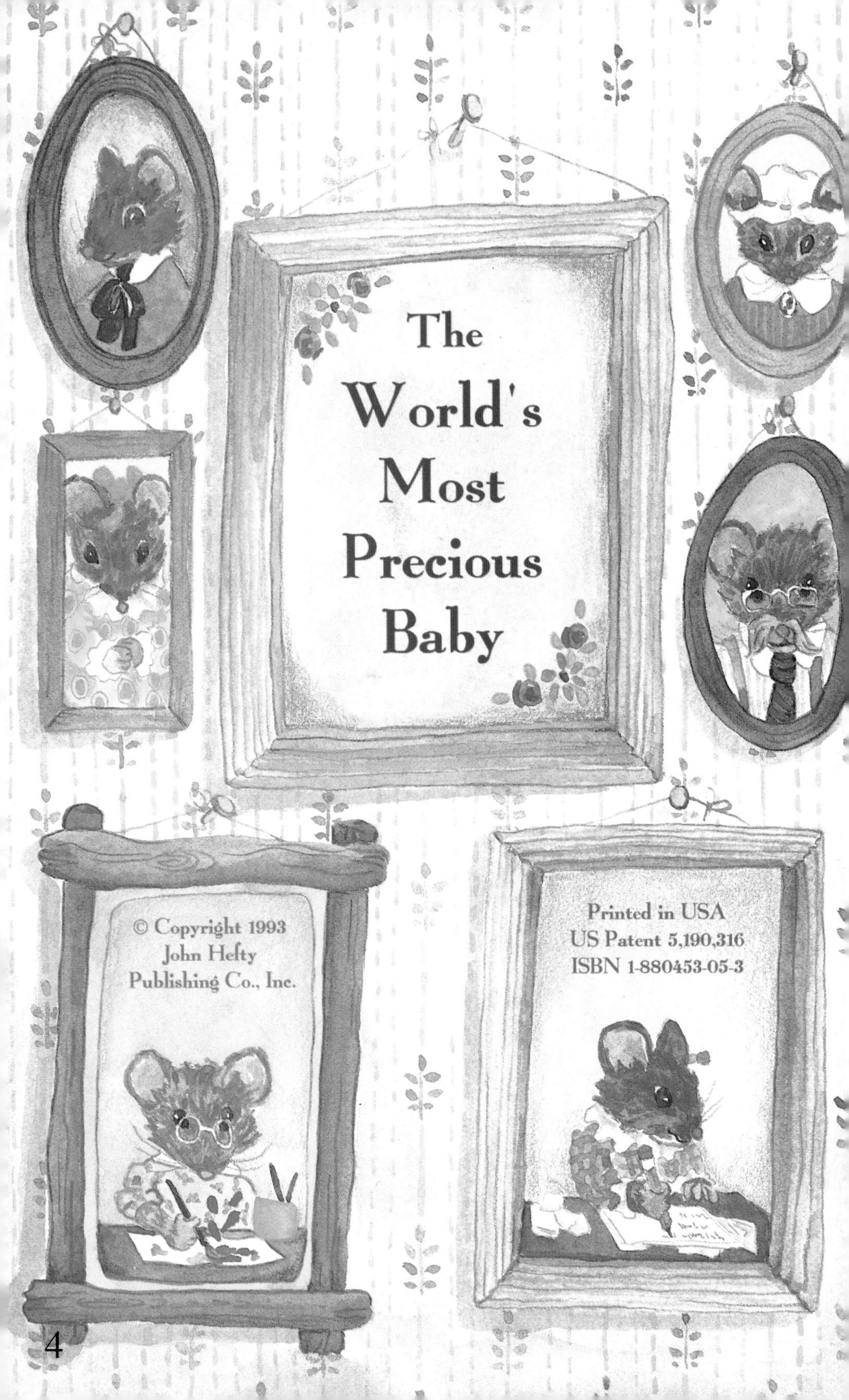

The World's Most Precious Baby

Printed in USA
US Patent 5,190,316
ISBN 1-880453-05-3

Story by
Rita T. Hefty
&
Emily T. Peterson
Illustrated by
Lyn Gray Rackley

Where do precious little babies come from?

Well, some people say adorable
little babies like me are found
under cabbage leaves...

And, some people say
that storks deliver babies in
neat little packages.

It has even
been said that
babies
are a very special gift
from Heaven,
carried by angels,
and placed gently
in
their mother's arms.

Place
"Where Baby Was Born"
Here

Place
Sticker
Here
Place
Sticker
Here
Place
Sticker
Here
Place
"Doctor" Sticker
Here

Place
"Weight" Paragraph
Here

Next I was carefully measured.
Wow! This is a lot of activity for the first day of a baby's life. I wonder if every day will be this busy.

Place Sticker Here

As I was placed in the arms of a very beautiful woman, I heard her say, "You are truly the world's most precious baby."

It felt wonderful
to be held so warmly
and lovingly. As we quietly
sat and watched each other, I
realized that this was my mommy.

Place Sticker "C" Here
Place Sticker "B" Here
Place Sticker "A" Here
Place Sticker Here

Place
Sticker
Here
Place
"Visitors" Sticker
Here

There were a lot of pictures taken of me. Some of them were really cute, and some looked a little silly.

I heard mommy say she chose the best picture of me to put with our family photo collection. I look quite adorable, don't you think?

We enjoyed
each and every day together. I loved to
have gentle lullabies sung to me. I always
fell asleep to "Rock-a-bye Baby."

Place
Sticker
Here
A G H
A F
Place
Sticker
Here

Bath time was great!
I loved to splash
the water, and even
when I got mommy wet,
she just laughed.

She really
laughed when I made
faces at the new
foods she fed me.

Every day is a new and exciting adventure. Mommy says it won't be long before I'm running and playing with the big kids. I can't wait, but I can tell she thinks I'm growing up too fast.

I keep mommy so busy
she barely has time to write to her friends
about my arrival.
Yes, I know the stork didn't bring me here,
and I wasn't found under a cabbage leaf...

I'm here by the miracle
of a very special love, and that makes me
the world's most precious baby.

Important Dates

First Bath____________________________
Sleeps All Night______________________
First Doctor's Visit____________________
First Smile___________________________
Rolls Over___________________________
Sits Alone____________________________
Crawls_______________________________
Pulls Self Up_________________________
First Word____________________________
First Tooth___________________________
First Steps____________________________
First Haircut__________________________